dramascripts

Adam's Ark

by

Harold Hodgson

**MACMILLAN
EDUCATION**

First published 1975
Reprinted 1976, 1977 (twice), 1979, 1981, 1982 (twice),
1983, 1984, 1985, 1986, 1987

Published by
MACMILLAN EDUCATION LTD
Houndmills, Basingstoke, Hampshire RG21 2XS
and London
Companies and representatives
throughout the world

Printed in Hong Kong

ISBN 0-333-18244-8

FOREWORD

DRAMASCRIPTS are intended for use in secondary schools, amateur theatrical groups and youth clubs, and some will be enjoyed by young people who are still at primary school. They may be used in a variety of ways: read privately for pleasure or aloud in groups; acted in the classroom, church hall or youth club, or in public performances.

Here is a play that was not written for junior forms. ADAM'S ARK by Harold Hodgson shows a group of young (teenage) people in an extraordinary situation – because they happen to be underground, in a specially contrived shelter, they manage to survive a nuclear explosion that wipes out virtually everyone else for hundreds of miles around. The subject, which could be a depressing one, is handled by the author with such skill that the play is, instead, both amusing and inspiring.

GUY WILLIAMS
Advisory Editor

THE CHARACTERS

TED BOYLE, a teacher
ADAM BURROUGHS, a waterworks engineer
MARY BURROUGHS, his wife
GILLIAN
TRACY
LYNDA
SHARON
SUSAN
TERRY
JOHN   members of a school party
PHILIP   on a visit to the waterworks
ALAN
FIRST GIRL
SECOND GIRL
FIRST BOY
SECOND BOY
THIRD BOY
DOCTOR AINSWORTH
THE COLONEL
TWO SOLDIERS

THE SCENES

ADAM'S ARK

ACT ONE

Scene 1

The interior of R.S.G. 21, situated underground, somewhere in the northern counties. It is the main communal room, which is entered from outside through a heavy door, down a short flight of steps. At one side, two doors lead off to a dormitory and kitchen. On the opposite side are doors to toilets and a second dormitory. Ventilation trunking, with louvres, runs the length of the wall. The room is sparsely furnished with two formica tables and 'utility' chairs. A telephone, a radio set and a panel of dials are located on a metal desk. The letters R.S.G. 21 are painted in white over the central door. The walls are a drab olive-green.

(At the rise of the curtain the room is empty and in darkness. Angry voices are heard off-stage. The door is flung open and from the off-stage lighting in the outer corridor we see a man being bundled forcibly into the room by other figures crowding him in.)

A Voice. Where are the lights?
Another Voice. Try the wall.

(The lights go up to reveal **Adam Burroughs** *getting up off the floor. He is a burly man in his fifties. A windcheater covers his slacks and sweater. Coming down the steps is* **Ted Boyle**, *a teacher in his late twenties. He is followed by a number of teenagers, the boys first. The boys and girls are, in the main, in school uniform. There is a buzz of comment in the room.* 'It's a shelter.' 'Like a prison.' 'Just like school.' *Some laughter.)*

Burroughs *(Authoritatively)*. You'll suffer for this. This is government property and you're trespassing.
Boyle. It's an R.S.G., isn't it?

1

Philip. What's an R.S.G., sir?

(A few of the boys and girls are wandering into the room but others stay on the steps with most of the girls)

Burroughs. You're in charge of this lot. The visit's over. Get 'em into their bus and off back to school. Or their homes.

Boyle. There may be no homes to go back to.

Burroughs. I can't help that. I've got my job to do. And there's no room in here for a load of kids.

Philip. Hey, sir! What is an R.S.G.? It's got it up there. *(Pointing to lettering)*

Boyle. It's a shelter against atom bombs. *(To* **Burroughs***)* Look, I can't take them back till I know what I'm taking them back to. Have the bombs been dropped?

Burroughs. They're on their way. That's my information.

Terry. Are they bombing us, sir?

Boyle. Maybe. We'll know soon.

Gillian. Does that mean our homes'll go?

Boyle. That depends. It's not going to be healthy anywhere, no matter where they drop.

Burroughs *(Moving to steps)*. Is that outer door closed?

Tracy. No.

Burroughs. Let me up.

(He pushes through and goes out briefly. **Boyle** *is besieged by questions.)*

Susan. What are we going to do, sir?

Lynda. Will our mums and dads be O.K.?

First Boy. Are we going back now, sir?

Boyle. Look. Look. We don't even know it's happened yet. It may be a false alarm.

John. It'll be a false alarm. You'll see. They wouldn't start anything.

Boyle. We'll wait here for as long as we can. Till we get some news.

Burroughs *(Returning and speaking from steps)*. That's just as long as you can wait. Till there's some news. Then you go. Out of my way.

(He pushes down the steps towards the telephone)

Philip. Listen to the tough guy.

(Second and Third Boys mime shooting one another and speak in mock-American accents)

Third Boy. Are you going quietly?

Second Boy. Go for your gun, cop. *(He clutches his stomach)* Ya got me in de guts, ya doity rat.

Burroughs. You can laugh, sonny. That's just what I'm supposed to do.

(He rattles the telephone impatiently)

Boyle. Stop fooling, you lot. *(To* **Burroughs***)* What do you mean by that?

Burroughs. I mean just what I said. I'm authorised to shoot anyone illegally entering this bunker in times of emergency. Anyone – whether he's the enemy or a schoolkid being shown round the reservoir or the schoolmaster in charge of him. *(Rattling the phone)* Damn! Why doesn't she hear?

Boyle. You mean you'll turn us out at gunpoint if the bombs drop.

Burroughs. Just that.

Terry. Who's it for, then?

Burroughs. It's for the V.I.P.s, laddie. The emergency controllers. The ones whose job is to clean up the mess, direct the emergency services.

Boyle. You think there'll be anything left to clean up?

Burroughs. There may be. I wouldn't ... Hello, hello, Mary? Adam here. Listen. Drop everything right now and get over to the bunker. Now. The balloon's gone up. Of course I'm not joking. Get over here right away.

(He puts the phone down and begins operating the short-wave radio)

Boyle. The four-minute warning, eh?

Burroughs *(Working the set)*. Yes. And not much of the four minutes left either.

Third Boy. What's that mean, sir?

Boyle. It means we should know in less than four minutes whether the bomb has dropped.

Gillian. You mean it's actually happening, sir?

John. It'll be a rehearsal. They wouldn't start a megatonic war.

3

(The radio begins to crackle and a distorted voice is heard)

Burroughs. Shut up. We'll know soon enough.
Radio. R.S.G. control. This is R.S.G. control. R.S.G. control calling all
R.S.G. stations. Keep your channels open for an important
announcement. I repeat. This is R.S.G. control calling all R.S.G.
stations. Keep your channels open for an important announcement.

(There is an expectant pause)

Tracy. They can't be sending the bombs.
Susan. What'll we do, sir?
Burroughs. Just keep quiet and listen.
Radio. R.S.G. control calling all R.S.G. stations. Stand by for an
important announcement from the Deputy Controller. Stand by.
(Voice changes) This is your Deputy Controller. Code word
Doomsday. Code word Doomsday. Reports from Fylingdales state
that enemy rockets were launched at 14.30 hours. Their course is
being monitored but everything indicates a major attack on this
country. Our own forces are retaliating. Alert all personnel to join
their stations, wherever possible. Individual stations to report
details of enemy attack on their areas using their own channels in
accordance with Emergency Code Two. This channel to be kept
open at all times except when transmitting. I repeat. This is your
Deputy Controller. Code word Doomsday, code word Doomsday.
Reports from Fylingdales ...

(Burroughs *turns down the radio to a murmur, picks up the phone,*
dials and waits)

Burroughs. Well, you heard it. Now, will you get out?
Boyle. Now?
Sharon. Sir, he's not going to send us out to be bombed, is he?
Boyle. He's going to try.
Burroughs *(Still at the telephone)*. Look, I don't want to seem hard on
you kids, but I have my orders.
Terry *(Moving to him)*. You mean you'd turn us out in the open to be
bombed?
Burroughs. They're not going to drop their bombs on a reservoir way
out in the hills. The cities'll get it.

4

Terry. Our homes you mean.

Gillian. Oh, no!

Boyle. We're not going. We're staying here.

Burroughs. Look, I've told you my orders. I shoot anyone invading this
bunker illegally.

Philip. He hasn't got a gun.

Burroughs (*Putting down phone and opening drawer in desk*). No, but I
can soon get one. (*Takes out revolver*) Now, you're all going out
through that door and into the tunnel. You can stay there for a
little while if you like. You'll have some protection from the shock
waves, from the initial blast and the heat. Then I advise you to get
in that school bus of yours and head north. Don't try going back
home, it won't be a pretty sight. Get to hell out of the area and
good luck to you.

Boyle. We're not going.

Alan. That's it, sir. Stand up to him.

Burroughs. He won't stand up to a bullet. Now, take your party and go
– quietly.

(*He moves threateningly towards* **Boyle**. **Terry** *is on his left.*
Margaret Burroughs *enters: she stands at the door, distraught.*)

Mrs Burroughs. Adam. Adam. I've seen it – the cloud. Over the hill,
Manchester way. They've ... Adam, look out! Adam!

(**Terry** *launches himself at* **Burroughs** *and grabs the arm holding
the gun.* **Boyle** *closes in and also grapples with him. The gun goes
off harmlessly into the air and falls from* **Burroughs'** *grasp.* **Alan**
picks it up and gives it to **Boyle** *as the scuffle subsides.*)

Boyle. Is anybody hurt?

Alan. The gun went off in the air, sir.

Mrs Burroughs (*Approaching* **Burroughs**). Are you all right, love?

Burroughs. Yes, I'm all right.

Boyle. You might have killed someone.

Burroughs. But I didn't. And I don't think I would. The gun went off
because you jumped me. I wouldn't have fired. I don't think so
anyway. I was just trying to get you out.

Third Boy. Chuck him out, sir.

Second Boy. Yeah, let's chuck him out, and his missus.

5

Boyle. There's no need for that. We may need him.

Burroughs. You're right there, teacher. You can't run this place without me. What do you lot know about survival in an atomic attack?

Boyle. Nothing, that's true. But then nobody ever told us what to do. We weren't expected to survive, were we?

Burroughs. Some will survive. It's my job, along with others, to help them. When the others arrive they'll maybe make you see sense.

Boyle. We'll see about that when they arrive – if they arrive – and if we let them in.

Terry. Why let them in, sir? First come, first served.

John. Yes, why should we be chucked out for a bunch of old men?

Burroughs. What you call the old men will include doctors to help the wounded. And some of those wounded may include your schoolmates – and your parents.

First Girl. I don't want to stay here anyway. I want to go home.

Second Girl. So do I.

Boyle. We can't go back till we know what the damage is. *(To* **Burroughs***)* When will you know?

Burroughs. I'll try to contact the other R.S.G.s. *(Crosses to radio, speaking to his wife)* You said that cloud was Manchester way, love?

Mrs Burroughs. Near enough.

Burroughs *(Throwing switches to transmit, and operating dials)*. We'll try them first. R.S.G. 24? This is R.S.G. 21. Are you receiving me? Over.

(There is no reply. He tries again.)

R.S.G. 24? This is R.S.G. 21. Are you receiving me? Over.

Radio. R.S.G. 21? This is R.S.G. 24. I am receiving you. How is it in your area? Report please. Over.

Burroughs. No enemy action yet but I haven't yet checked the scanner, or radiation levels. Post is not effective yet as I am the only operative. I have to report intruders in the post. Over.

Radio. You know the drill, 21. Carry it out. Over.

Burroughs. I'm afraid that is not possible at the moment. How are things your area? Over.

Radio. Things are hotting up here. Attack on the area estimated at fifty megatons. We are assuming our post will be ineffective owing to radiation levels. Over.

Burroughs. Thank you, 24. Over and out.

Mrs Burroughs. It's a bad attack, Adam, isn't it?

Burroughs. Bad enough. There won't be much of Manchester left standing. *(To* **Boyle***)* Where are you from? Little Hulton was it?

Boyle. Yes.

Burroughs. That's too near Manchester for comfort. I don't want to sound too pessimistic but the heat will have started fires and the radiation levels are likely to be near-lethal.

Third Boy. What does that mean?

Boyle. It means we'd be most unwise to go back home, Tom.

Third Boy. But I can't just stay here when my mum may be lying there badly burnt.

First Girl. I've got to go back too. I can't just stay here and do nothing.

Burroughs. Look, I've been trying to get you lot out of here ever since you burst in on me, but I don't advise you to head for Manchester. You'd just be walking into danger. Maybe certain death. Get into your bus and head north. It's going to be too hot for comfort up top even here.

(The boys and girls have all crept into the room by now and are sitting on chairs, tables and steps. **Boyle** *moves to stand on the steps.)*

Boyle. Now listen carefully, everyone. If we leave this shelter we put ourselves in danger of death from radiation. And it'll be a slow death. If we go back home, we're merely going to bring that death nearer. And, I'm sorry to have to say this, but it's extremely unlikely that we can save anyone at home who has been subject to intense radiation. You may think it's easy for me to say this because I'm not married and I've no one to go back to. But if you go back you're probably making a useless journey and putting yourselves in real danger. I strongly advise you to stay here. I'm sure your parents would wish it. They wouldn't want you to sacrifice yourselves out of a mistaken sense of duty. For God's sake stay here where you're safe – for the moment, anyway.

First Girl. I still want to go back, sir.

Third Boy. My mind's made up, sir. I'm going back. I can drive the old bus. Who's coming? We'll collect our mums and dads and be back here inside a couple of hours.

Burroughs. Now look. This is just foolish. You can't go bringing loads of sick and wounded people back here. Don't you understand that

7

you'll only be bringing them here to die? They can't possibly survive. This place is built to support about a dozen people, not an army.

Terry. There's nothing I can do about my mum and dad. They both work in Salford and I suppose ... well ... I suppose they've had it ... and I ... But that's no reason why those who feel they can do something about it shouldn't try, and good luck to them. And if they get back I vote we take them in and do our best for them.

Boyle. I can't stop anyone going back who feels he must but I strongly advise you not to, because I honestly don't think we shall see you again. I mean that.

Third Boy. Well, I think there'll be plenty of survivors.

Second Boy. Yeah, and another thing, the longer we leave it, the worse it'll get for anybody at home. The sooner we get away and back again the better. I vote we go now. Tom'll drive us, won't you, Tom?

Third Boy. Sure I will. You can trust me. Never had an accident yet.

Boyle. You've never been on the road yet, Tom. And don't forget the roads may be swarming with people getting out as fast as they can.

Third Boy. I'll risk it, sir.

(He heads for the door and turns on the steps)

Well, who's coming with me? Anybody?

Second Boy *(Moving)*. Me for one.

First Boy. And me.

First Girl. Me too. I've got to find out what's happened.

Second Girl. I'm going as well.

Alan. I think you should take Mr Boyle's advice and stay – for the time being, anyway.

Third Boy. If we wait they'll all be dead. Anybody else coming?

Susan. I don't know what to do for the best.

Boyle. Stay here, Susan. I don't think there's anything they'll be able to do.

Third Boy. We'll have a damn' good try. Let's not waste any more time arguing. Off we go.

(He goes out followed by **First** *and* **Second Boys**, *and* **First** *and* **Second Girls***)*

Boyle. Good luck to you.

Burroughs. They'll need it.

Boyle *(Calling after them)*. Get back as soon as you can. You can't afford to hang around.

Susan *(Crying)*. It doesn't seem right. They're trying to do something and we just sit here safe as houses. It's selfish.

Gillian. Come and sit down, love. *(Leads her to a chair)* I don't think we could do much if we went. We're not doctors. We wouldn't know what to do.

Susan. I could bring them back. My mum, at least.

Gillian. We still wouldn't be able to treat them.

Lynda. Well, I wouldn't go back for my dad. He hates me.

Boyle. Now come on, Lynda.

Lynda. No, I wouldn't. He's been rotten to me ever since my mum died.

Boyle. Well, maybe he had his reasons. *(Joking)* Can't have been easy bringing *you* up Lynda.

Lynda. I wasn't that bad. Not really. You know, I think Mr Boyle is right. When he says our parents wouldn't want us to risk our lives, bringing them back. I know my dad wouldn't. 'Go on,' he'd say. 'Look after Number One, lass.'

Burroughs *(Who has been listening to the muted radio)*. Shut up a minute, will you. I want to listen.

(Turns up radio)

Radio. ... on centres of dense population. Reports from all the major conurbations indicate heavy attacks. The Manchester/Liverpool area, the Birmingham complex, and especially the London area confirm this. Casualties are expected to be severe and it is likely that telephone services will be completely disrupted. All R.S.G.s should rely on police wavelengths for local communications. End of message. Out.

Boyle. It sounds bad, doesn't it?

Burroughs. Bad enough.

Mrs Burroughs. What'll happen, Adam?

Burroughs. I don't know yet, love. Without the telephone we're stymied. The only thing I can think of is to contact the police and check they're directing people to safe areas, wherever they are. Find out the general situation. What I can't understand is why nobody else has checked in. Doc Ainsworth should be here with his ambulances. And the Superintendent, and the Colonel.

9

Mrs Burroughs. Maybe they've just ... you know ...

Terry. Goners, you mean, don't you?

Burroughs. It's too early to say. After all, they weren't on the spot like us.

John. What do we do then?

Burroughs. We sit and wait, laddie.

(General movement to seats)

Tracy. I'm getting hungry.

Philip. And I could do with a fag.

Burroughs. There'll be no smoking in here, young fellow. The good air's too precious.

Mrs Burroughs. Shall I organise a cup of tea and a snack, Adam?

Burroughs. Good idea, love. Take a couple of girls to help you.

Mrs Burroughs *(Crossing to the kitchen)*. Anybody like to help?

Gillian *(To* **Susan***)*. Come on, let's give a hand, hey?

Susan *(Moving off with her and* **Mrs Burroughs***)*. O.K.

Boyle *(To* **Burroughs***)*. You mentioned good air. How do you make it good?

Burroughs. Air is blown through that trunking and out of the louvres. *(He points to the ventilation trunking)* There's a pretty sophisticated filtration system. Same with the water, only that shouldn't need filtering yet – it comes from an underground spring.

Boyle. And the power?

Burroughs. Hydroelectric. Works from the dam. Powers my own house as a matter of fact. Should last for years with just a minimum of maintenance.

Boyle. And food?

Burroughs. Plenty for the proper staff, but not enough to feed the five thousand. Dried and canned stuff mainly.

Philip. Are there any toilets here? I could use one.

Burroughs. That door there. *(Indicating the door.* **Philip** *crosses.)* Serves as a decontamination room as well. The other two rooms are for sleeping. *(To* **Philip***)* Remember, laddie, no smoking in these toilets.

*(***Philip** *makes a face behind his back and goes out)*

Boyle. I don't see what purpose all this serves, except to provide a convenient private air-raid shelter for a lot of V.I.P.s. What do you hope to do?

Burroughs. We're supposed to direct rescue and relief operations in our area. Organise evacuation. Direct hospital services. Bring in food where necessary. Bury the dead, I suppose.

Boyle. Do you honestly think there's much you can do?

Burroughs. Privately, I don't mind telling you now, I think it's a lot of wishful thinking. But I was the logical man to put in charge of this bunker and I'd have been a fool to turn down a comfortable private air-raid shelter. Now, excuse me, I must try the police wavelengths.

(He moves to the radio and begins operating.
Philip *enters.)*

Philip. Not a single word on the toilet walls. We'll have to alter that, won't we? 'Philip loves Lynda.' How's that for a start?

Lynda. Bighead.

Burroughs. This is R.S.G. 21 calling Police. Are you receiving me? Over.

(There is a silence)

Hello, Police. This is R.S.G. 21 calling. Are you receiving me? Over.

(Another silence)

I'll try later.

Sharon. Why not try your transistor, Tracy?

Tracy. Why don't you try your own?

Sharon. I didn't bring it, silly. That was my cassette recorder I was playing on the bus.

Tracy. All right. I'll have a go.

(She takes a small transistor from her bag and tries to find a station. There is an expectant silence but nothing is heard except static.)

Sharon. Try another station.

Tracy. I've tried them all. There's nothing.

John. Keep trying. Somebody must be alive somewhere.

(Mrs Burroughs enters, followed by the girls, carrying trays of cups of tea and biscuits which are handed round)

Mrs Burroughs. Tea's up. There's nothing to eat except biscuits, I'm afraid. Not till we open up the tins. It's powdered milk too, but we can't expect it straight from the cow, can we? Help yourselves to the biscuits. There are plenty more where those came from. Very British and all that, aren't we, Adam? In the middle of Armageddon, we have a cup of tea.

*(Before she finishes speaking, the door opens and **Dr Ainsworth**, a man in his late fifties, enters, looking grim and distraught)*

Burroughs. Doc! Good to see you. Is there anybody with you?
Dr Ainsworth. No.
Mrs Burroughs. You're just in time for a cup of tea, Jim.
Dr Ainsworth. I need more than tea, Mary. Adam, get me some of the radiation pills from the cabinet, will you? Bring them into the showers. I must get through the decontamination routine as soon as I can.

(Crosses to the toilet door)

Burroughs. Is it bad up top, Jim?
Dr Ainsworth. It's lethal, Adam. If I survive I'll start saying my prayers again.

Scene 2

Two days later. It is the end of the evening meal. All are seated at the tables apart from **Adam Burroughs** and **Dr Ainsworth**.

Boyle. That was very good, Susan. My compliments to the chef.
Philip. Yeah, very 'more-ish' that was. Very good, but I could have done with more.
Lynda. Gutsy!
Philip. In case you should ever marry me, Lynda, I should tell you, I'm very fond of my stomach.
Lynda. You'd have to be the last man on earth for me to marry you.

Philip. The way things are going, that could well happen.

Alan. Oh, stop rowing, you two. It was very nice, Susan.

Tracy. She was always teacher's pet in Cookery.

Sharon. That's more than I was. I used to burn everything.

Alan. That I can believe.

Sharon. Pig! No, but it's true. Some people are born to be domestic
slaves. I was born for higher things.

Terry. Like what?

Sharon. I was born to inspire some genius. Like Alan. You're the school
genius, aren't you, Alan? Everybody says you are.

Alan. Who am I to deny it? If I'm ever in need of inspiration, I'll let
you know, Sharon.

Boyle. Who's supposed to clear and who's doing the washing-up?

Terry. I'm on washing-up with Gillian. John and Tracy are clearing.

Gillian *(Rising and moving to kitchen,* **Terry** *following)*. Come on,
Terry. Get your pinny on.

Philip. Hey, they sound just like an old married couple, don't they?
Darby and Joan. My mum used to say that to my dad and he ...
well he ...

Boyle. Yes. Well, let's clear away, shall we? John, Tracy? *(They begin
clearing)* You know, I feel just like Philip when I've had a meal.
I'm dying for a fag.

Mrs Burroughs. I'm quite sure it wouldn't make any difference if you
had one, in spite of what Adam says. We've got a most efficient
Expelair system.

Boyle. Trouble is I've run out. I was very naughty last night, smoked
my last one in the toilets.

John. Write out a hundred times 'I must not smoke in the toilets'.

Boyle. I won't do it again, so I'll let myself off this time.

Lynda. Why don't you go out and get some, sir? Put on a white suit like
the doctor and Mr Burroughs and walk out and go in the first shop
and help yourself. Just think, everything's for free! You can walk
into any shop and you'll know the shopkeeper can't stop you
picking up anything you like, 'cos he's dead or dying. Like my dad,
like everybody except us, burrowing under the earth like rabbits.

Mrs Burroughs. Susan, I put two dinners in the oven for Adam and the
doctor. Would you like to see if they're all right?

Susan *(Leaving)*. Yes.

Mrs Burroughs. I'm worried about them, Ted. They should have been
back ages ago.

13

Boyle. Now come on Mrs B., they're only half an hour late. And they do have protection.

Mrs Burroughs. I'm not sure those white suits and air bottles are any protection against this horrible thing that's hit us. I don't even feel very safe underground.

Boyle. We're the lucky ones, Mrs B. From what the doctor says there aren't going to be many survivors up top.

Mrs Burroughs. That's what worries me. Do you suppose it's like this all over the world?

Boyle. I shouldn't think it'll be as bad as that. There must be lots of places untouched.

Mrs Burroughs. America. It'll be bad there, I suppose.

Boyle. Probably. But it's a big place. Why do you ask?

Mrs Burroughs. My son David's out there. Texas. They wanted doctors and they paid well, so he went. Married out there. We went over for the wedding, Adam and I. They have two children now, but I haven't seen them. I don't suppose ...

Boyle. Well, as I said, it's a big place.

(Voices are heard, off)

Lynda. That sounds like the Doc.

Sharon. Shall I get their dinner?

Mrs Burroughs. Not yet, love. They'll have to go through all that decontamination routine.

(The door opens and **Burroughs** *and* **Dr Ainsworth** *enter, wearing white overall suits, with oxygen bottles strapped to their backs.* **Burroughs** *has his helmet off;* **Dr Ainsworth** *is removing his, although hampered by his medical bag.)*

Burroughs. Hello, Mary. Sorry we're late. I hope you haven't been worrying. No, don't come near us. We're pretty hot. The radiation's worse than ever. We'll get under the showers.

*(***Burroughs** *and* **Dr Ainsworth** *go out hurriedly)*

John *(Who has been clearing the tables with* **Tracy***).* Move off you lot and let the workers wipe the tables.

Philip. What's the hurry? You're not going any place. Nor is anybody.

14

(They make a general move from the tables, taking chairs with them)

Lynda. If you're bored, why don't you take a walk outside?

Philip. What! And get myself ... Oh, very funny!

Sharon. No, you're right, Phil. It is boring. I was on washing-up yesterday and today I miss it. I never thought I'd miss washing-up.

Lynda. It's not exactly the swinging scene, is it? No radio, no telly. Not even a book to read.

Philip *(Taking out a pack of cards)*. We could have another game of pontoon.

Alan. Oh, no! We played pontoon all last night.

Sharon. And I lost all my money.

Philip. What use is money now? Let's play for love.

Lynda. Who wants your love?

Philip. Just say the word and it's all yours, darling. *(Sings)* 'If you were the only girl in the world, And I were the only boy ... '

(There is some half-hearted laughter)

Alan. It's nearly come to that, hasn't it though? I mean, just assume that nobody survives except us, then ... Well, we'd have to start the English race all over again.

Sharon. Hey, that's a thought, Alan. What do we do, draw names out of a hat?

Boyle. Look, if you're so bored, and it is boring I know, we'll have to draw up some programme. Sharon's got her cassette. We could have a dance.

Sharon. That won't last us long.

Boyle. If you like, I could organise some lessons. *(There is a chorus of groans)* Well, discussion groups ... or something.

John. What do we discuss, world affairs?

Tracy. 'Should there be universal world disarmament?' Bit late, isn't it?

Boyle. You suggest something, then.

Lynda. Let's settle for a game of cards. What about rummy?

Philip. Come on, folks. Better than sitting around biting your fingernails.

(There is a movement to the tables)

Mrs Burroughs. Sit at that one, will you? The doctor and Adam have to eat yet.

(She indicates one of the tables and arranges cutlery on the other)

Philip. Eyes down for the big game.

John. Are you playing, Mr Boyle?

Boyle. I'll have a game later, maybe. You'll have to teach me again. It's a long time since I played.

Philip *(In his 'posh' voice)*. He only plays bridge, you know.

Boyle. As a matter of fact I can play bridge. Our first lesson tomorrow will be 'Bridge for Beginners'.

*(**Burroughs** and **Dr Ainsworth** come in, having discarded their white suits. **The doctor** still carries his bag, which he leaves on the radio table.)*

Burroughs. Right. Bring on the food. I'm ravenous.

Mrs Burroughs. I'll go and get it, love. Sit down.

*(She goes out. **Dr Ainsworth** and **Burroughs** sit at the places set.)*

Boyle. How are things up top? You said the radiation was worse.

Burroughs. So it was. Much worse. Has to do with the wind direction, I think. We didn't get far.

Boyle. What kept you then?

Dr Ainsworth. My fault, Ted.

Burroughs. The Doc felt he had to carry his duties to the letter and check on the hospitals.

Boyle. And?

Dr Ainsworth. It's over. Finished. Those that aren't dead already are too sick to work. Everything is grinding rapidly to a halt. I suppose those who could get out have gone north. There were still a few people moving out in cars. Otherwise the road is clear.

(The card game is halted as the players listen)

Boyle. Will any of them escape?

Burroughs. As long as the wind stays in the south there's not much hope for people round here. As fast as they move north the radiation is following in the wind.

16

(Mrs Burroughs and Susan enter, each with a plate of food. They are followed by Terry and Gillian. All stand by the door and listen.)

Dr Ainsworth. If the wind changed, or it rained, there might be some hope in the short term. Not in the long run, though. Anyone subjected to massive radiation is going to die eventually.

Alan. Then all our folks at home . . .

Dr Ainsworth. I'm afraid you're all going to have to face the fact that you're not going to see your parents again. Nor any of your friends. Nor anything of the world you knew.

Tracy. It doesn't seem possible.

John. Not for everything to be finished.

Sharon *(Crying)*. Everybody dying.

Philip. And we're alive and kicking.

Lynda. It doesn't seem fair.

Dr Ainsworth. There's no need to feel guilty about it. You're the lucky ones. With more luck and patience you may survive. But it's going to be a long wait.

Alan. What do you mean, a long wait?

Dr Ainsworth. I mean you're going to have to live, or exist if you prefer it, in this shelter until it's safe to emerge.

Boyle. And how long is that likely to be?

Dr Ainsworth. I can't tell. But it'll be months rather than days. We have to wait for the winds to change, for the rains to come, for the earth and sky to be washed clean. And I don't know how long that will take.

Terry. You mean we're going to have to spend months in this rabbit warren?

Dr Ainsworth. That's the only way you'll survive.

Mrs Burroughs. Now come on. You two won't survive unless you eat.

(She and Susan bring the plates. Burroughs and Dr Ainsworth eat.)

Terry. How will we know when it's safe to leave?

Dr Ainsworth *(Between mouthfuls)*. The geiger counter up top *(Gestures with his fork)* will tell us when it's safe here . . . For the rest we'll have to rely on other R.S.G.s . . . They'll report on their areas . . . assuming they're in operation.

Gillian. And we go on living here for months.

Dr Ainsworth. For as long as it takes, or the food lasts.

17

Boyle. We're like those shipwrecked sailors, aren't we? So much food divided by x number of days. Only what is the value of x? How many days before that liner picks us up?

Dr Ainsworth. There'll be no liner, Ted. We've got to make a landfall ourselves. We've got to assume we're on our own. Nobody to pick us up.

Susan *(Hesitantly)*. Isn't there plenty of food ...?

Dr Ainsworth. Where?

Susan. Up there.

Dr Ainsworth. No food up there is worth eating once it's been subjected to radiation.

Burroughs. There's supposed to be food in there for twelve people for one year. That's what my inventory says. How many are we?

Mrs Burroughs. There are thirteen of us.

Burroughs. I hope nobody's superstitious. If you don't like eating thirteen to the table you'll have to get out.

Lynda. I'm superstitious – but I'm staying all the same.

Boyle. We've enough food for a year then – more or less.

Burroughs. Unless anyone else turns up, and that's not likely now.

Dr Ainsworth. If anyone else should turn up now, Adam, we'd have to turn him out.

Burroughs. Why, Jim?

Dr Ainsworth. Because we'd be harbouring a little package of radiation. A human body giving off lethal radiation until it died, and even after.

Alan. So it's just us.

Dr Ainsworth. That's it. Thirteen lucky people.

Sharon. And we stay here for a year?

Dr Ainsworth. Maybe.

Sharon. What will we do for a year?

Boyle. We're going to have to exercise a lot of patience, Sharon.

Lynda. It'll take all my patience to live with that one for a year.

(She indicates **Philip***)*

Philip. You'll learn to love me, darling.

Lynda. Huh!

Terry. Hey, listen. There's somebody outside.

Burroughs. In the passage?

Terry. Yes.

18

(All eyes focus on the door which opens to reveal the **Third Boy**, **Tom**. *He can barely stand and is obviously very sick.)*

Boyle. Tom! You made it.

Third Boy. Just about.

Boyle *(Moving to him)*. Are you all right?

Dr Ainsworth *(Savagely)*. Don't touch him. Any of you.

Boyle. We can't just ...

Dr Ainsworth. He's lethal! A leper! Get to your quarters. All of you. I'll deal with him.

(They reluctantly move off to their respective dormitories. **Terry** *and* **Gillian** *go back to the kitchen.)*

Go on. Quickly. You too, Mary. Adam, you can stay and give me a hand.

Boyle. I'll stay as well.

Dr Ainsworth. All right, if you must. It's your own risk.

Burroughs. What shall we do with him?

Dr Ainsworth. Decontamination first. Under the showers with him. Follow me ... Tom, is it?

Third Boy. Yes. What's ...

Dr Ainsworth *(To Boyle who is moving to help)*. Leave him alone. Let him walk on his own. Come on, son.

(Dr Ainsworth leads him off to the showers. **Tom** *follows weakly.)*

Boyle. Can the Doc do anything?

Burroughs. I doubt it. Make it easier for him, no doubt.

Boyle. Sedate him you mean?

Burroughs. Put him out of his misery, more likely.

Boyle. You don't mean ... kill him?

Burroughs. Let's call it euthanasia ... it sounds better.

Boyle. But it's still murder.

Burroughs. See the Doc's little black bag there? That's just about all he's got in it. Mercy drugs, they're called. One pill is supposed to make you as drunk as a lord and then you gradually slip into a stupor ... and you don't waken up. That's what's supposed to happen, but I don't expect anybody reported back on the effects.

Boyle. Is there nothing else we can do?

19

Burroughs. The lad's had two days of intense radiation. You heard what the Doc said earlier. We can't afford to harbour anyone like that.

*(*Dr Ainsworth *enters and picks up his bag)*

Dr Ainsworth. He's under the shower now. I've put his clothes in the disposal chute. Get something to cover him with, Adam.
Boyle *(Bitterly)*. A winding sheet?
Dr Ainsworth *(Sadly)*. It would be appropriate, Ted. There's nothing I can do for him. He should have stayed here with the rest of you.
Burroughs. Did he find his parents?
Dr Ainsworth. His mother, anyway. I gather he watched her die. He's not very coherent and he's vomiting most of the time.
Boyle. What will you do?
Burroughs. I've been telling him about your little pills, Jim.
Dr Ainsworth. Oh, I see. There's nothing else to do, Ted, believe me. We have to think of all the others. It's not pleasant, but you don't have to watch. Adam and I will attend to it. We've had a little more time to think this thing through.
Boyle. How bad is he?
Dr Ainsworth. Very bad. It's a wonder he got back here. He'll be dead anyway inside twenty-four hours. We can't afford to wait that long.
Boyle. How will you . . . bury him?
Dr Ainsworth. Leave that to us, Ted.

(He moves to the door)

Boyle. No, I'll give you a hand.
Burroughs. No need to, Ted. Doc and I can manage.
Boyle. I think I'd better. He was my responsibility. Maybe I should have forced them all to stay. *(He follows* **Dr Ainsworth** *out)*
Burroughs. You tried to persuade him, Ted. You couldn't do any more.

(He follows. The stage is empty for a moment, then **Gillian** *and* **Terry** *come in, from the kitchen.)*

Gillian. Nobody here.
Terry. They'll be in the showers.
Gillian. I suppose we ought to join the others, like the Doc ordered.

20

Terry *(Taking her hand)*. Let's have a minute to ourselves. We don't get much opportunity. *(He pulls her to him)*

Gillian *(Resisting)*. Not now, Terry. Somebody might come in. And it doesn't seem right with Tom ... Do you think he'll be all right, Terry?

Terry. No. He's dying. Didn't you see his face?

Gillian. Sort of glazed look he had.

Terry. He's bound to be dying if what the Doc said is true.

Gillian. I wonder if he found his mum and dad.

Terry. Can't have done or he'd have brought them back.

Gillian. That means that our ... Oh, Terry, I don't like to say it.

Terry *(Comforting her)*. We've got to face it, love. We're not going to see them again, ever. It's just you and me now. They'd have been pleased about that, I'm sure.

Gillian. My mum would. She always liked you, Terry.

Terry. You know what Alan was talking about earlier, about starting the English race all over again.

Gillian. Yes.

Terry. Well, I know he was partly joking but ... I'd like to think that we ... well that we were two of the first ...

Gillian. Are you proposing to me, Terry Heslop?

Terry. Sort of.

Gillian. The answer's 'Yes'. *(She gives him a quick kiss)* Right, now you ought to join the other boys and I'd better get back to the girls. Heaven knows what they'll be saying behind my back.

(She pushes him away and then goes to dormitory door, where she turns to blow him a kiss)

Bye, love. And thanks. I think you'll make a marvellous husband.

(They both go out)

21

ACT TWO

Scene 1

Eight months later. The R.S.G. is much the same as in the previous
scenes, apart from some rearrangement of furniture. There is a large
map of the British Isles on the wall near the radio. It is marked with red
flags to indicate highly radioactive areas. It is early morning. **Adam
Burroughs** sits at the radio-table writing in a log book and studying a
large map. He is wearing a white overall-suit but not the helmet and
gloves.

(*Mrs Burroughs comes in, wearing a dressing gown, and carrying a
cup of tea*)

Mrs Burroughs. I thought you'd like a cup of tea, Adam.

(*She takes it to him*)

Burroughs. Thanks, Mary. Have you got one for Ted? He's coming with
   me to do the labouring.
Mrs Burroughs (*Concerned*). You won't be long, will you, Adam?
Burroughs. Don't worry, love. It shouldn't take more than twenty
   minutes if everything goes O.K. Don't forget I'll be switching over
   to the batteries while we fix the generator so don't go using the
   cooker or any heaters. I don't want the batteries draining.
Mrs Burroughs. Right-o, love. I'll get Ted's tea.

(*She goes out. There is a pause during which* **Burroughs** *continues
writing.* **Ted** *comes in, wearing a white overall-suit, carrying the
helmet.*)

Boyle. Ready, Adam.
Burroughs (*Finishing writing*). Good. We'll have a cup of tea and then
   go. Mary's just bringing yours. Anyone else stirring?
Boyle. Doc opened one eye and then went back to sleep. The others are

22

all snoring. Except Terry. He wasn't in his bunk. Have you seen him?

Burroughs. No.

(Mrs Burroughs enters with Ted's cup of tea)

Mrs Burroughs. There you are, Ted. Here's your cup of tea. *(Giving it to him)* Now take care of my husband, won't you. I'd be lost without him.

Boyle. Wouldn't we all? I'm sure I wouldn't know how to fix hydro-electric generators when they grow temperamental.

Mrs Burroughs. He works too hard. He's been up since the crack of dawn Not that we ever see the dawn, but you know what I mean.

Burroughs. She calls eight o'clock the crack of dawn. *(To Ted)* I had to get up a bit earlier. I'd arranged to contact the Welsh group at seven-thirty. Their survey figures are through. I've been plotting them on the map. Quite encouraging really. They're thinking of leaving the bunker when they've got themselves organised. The radiation seems to be down to an acceptable level over a wide area round Aberystwyth even with an east wind.

Boyle. So we could join them.

Burroughs. If we can find that way through. There's still a band of heavy radiation stretching from Liverpool to Sheffield and no way through that I can see, not without radiation suits for everyone, which we haven't got.

Boyle. By sea?

Burroughs. My navigational know-how wouldn't get me round a duck pond. How's yours?

Boyle. About the same.

Mrs Burroughs. I don't know why we don't settle for the Lake District. Join those two fellows at Lancaster.

Burroughs. Simply because we've no radiation figures for the whole area. They both strike me as being too scared to venture out yet. After all, the radiation levels in Lancaster are every bit as encouraging as the Welsh. There doesn't seem any reason to expect anything but a further improvement up in the Lakes.

Boyle. Why don't we survey it ourselves? We could be there in a couple of hours.

Mrs Burroughs. Why don't we, Adam?

Burroughs. The Welsh group is bigger – more of a community when we

23

do settle down on top. Anyway, there's no immediate hurry. Nothing pushing us until the food gets short. If you've finished your tea, Ted, we'll be on our way.

(They begin to put on their helmets)

Boyle. Do we really need these? I feel like a kid playing at spacemen.
Burroughs. We're probably safe enough. I do it to please Mary who thinks I'll drop down dead if I take a breath of fresh air.
Mrs Burroughs. Fresh air, he says! I wonder if there's any left anywhere.
Boyle. Oh, have you seen Terry, Mrs B? He's not in his bunk.
Mrs Burroughs. I haven't, love. Probably sneaked off to be alone with Gillian, though where they find to hide themselves in this hole I don't know.
Boyle. I suspect he may have gone up top. They're all getting restless, Terry in particular.
Mrs Burroughs. Well he has his reasons, hasn't he? Now off you go and look after Adam.
Boyle. I will. See you soon.

*(Fastens his helmet and goes. As he goes out, **Gillian** enters. She walks heavily and is obviously very pregnant.)*

Gillian. Good morning, Mrs B. Was that Terry?
Mrs Burroughs. No, love. It was Ted. He's gone off to give Adam a hand with the generators. What made you think it might be Terry? Ted's just been enquiring after him – says he's not in his bunk.
Gillian *(Sitting)*. I'm worried about him, Mrs B. I think he may have gone out again.
Mrs Burroughs. Again?
Gillian. He was out last week. I happened to say I fancied some tinned peaches and he sneaked off down to the village and brought me four tins.
Mrs Burroughs. Did you eat them?
Gillian. No. I think I was fancying bananas by the time he brought them. Anyway, I thought they might damage the baby. You know ... if they were still – what do they say? – hot.
Mrs Burroughs *(Sitting)*. And why do you suspect that Terry's out again?
Gillian. I happened to say I could do with some proper smocks now that

24

I'm getting so big. So Terry said he'd see to it. Well, I knew what he meant so I begged him not to go out again.

Mrs Burroughs. And what did he say?

Gillian. He said Mr Burroughs and the doctor were being far too cautious and it was safe enough for anybody to go out now and ...

Mrs Burroughs. And what?

Gillian. Well, he said nobody had the right to keep us in if we wanted to leave. And he wasn't going to be treated like a kid in a schoolroom.

Mrs Burroughs. He's not all that long out of the schoolroom, is he?

Gillian. It's not like Terry to talk like that, Mrs B. He usually has plenty of common sense and he's usually very polite. It's just ... well being a father ... or nearly ... he feels he ought to have me out of here. In some place where we'd have a proper home of our own. It's not easy being sort of married and living with a lot of other people.

Mrs Burroughs. Well, my dear, Adam and I are 'sort of married' and we manage to live with all the rest of you.

Gillian. It's different for you, you've ... you've had all your young life together. You know what I mean.

Mrs Burroughs. I know, love. All young couples should have a place of their own.

Gillian *(Tearful)*. And Terry gets furious when some of the others make jokes about the baby. It's not our fault we can't get married, is it?

Mrs Burroughs. Of course it isn't, love. Stop fretting about it.

(Susan comes in with a towel)

Susan. Morning, Mrs B. Where is everybody?

Mrs Burroughs. Adam and Ted are doing something to the generator.

Susan. Oh, yes. No breakfast till they've finished.

(She goes into the bathroom. As she disappears, Philip enters heading in the same direction.)

Mrs Burroughs. You can't go in there, young man. Susan's getting washed.

Philip *(Sitting)*. And I thought I was the early bird.

Lynda *(Coming in)*. You're the worm.

(She also goes into the bathroom)

25

Philip. Why is everybody up and about so early? Mr Burroughs and
Mr Boyle are up and so is Terry.

Mrs Burroughs. Adam and Ted are working on the generator. And
what's all this about Terry? Gillian thinks he may have gone
outside.

Philip *(To* **Gillian***)*. Does Mrs B. know?

Gillian. Yes. I told her. I was worried about Terry.

Mrs Burroughs. Has he gone outside?

Philip. I wouldn't be surprised. He was talking about it last night. Said
he might sneak off to the village if he could wake up early.
Something for Gill, I think.

Gillian. I knew it. *(To* **Mrs Burroughs***)* You don't have to tell the doctor
and Mr Burroughs, do you? He might get into trouble. I mean,
they wouldn't try to throw him out, would they?

Mrs Burroughs. Of course they wouldn't. Not now. Adam's always
telling me it's safe enough to go out without any protection. Only
I make him put a suit on, to be on the safe side. I don't see any
sense in taking risks until we have to. That's why Terry's being
silly.

Philip. Hey, Gill, do you remember Terry describing what it was like
outside? Like a ghost town the village was, he said. Not a sound
except some bits of paper blowing round in a corner and a door
banging in the wind. And not a person in sight and not an animal.
Just a few birds floating around. The silence, he said. You never
heard anything like the silence.

*(There is a thoughtful pause and then a burst of pop music comes
from the girls' dormitory. The volume increases as* **Sharon** *comes in
with her cassette recorder and a towel.)*

Mrs Burroughs *(Shouting)*. Turn it down, Sharon. *(***Sharon** *obliges)*
You'll wake everybody up. We don't want them all swarming out
hungry for breakfast. It won't be ready for a while.

Sharon. I'll turn it off then. *(She does)* Save the batteries.

Mrs Burroughs. I thought the batteries were finished long ago.

Sharon. Well they were, but Terry ... Oh, I forgot.

Gillian. Mrs B. knows about Terry going out.

Mrs Burroughs. So he got batteries as well as tinned peaches. Quite the
little forager, isn't he? Well, he's out foraging again by all accounts.
I hope he doesn't bring back more batteries. I'd got used to the
silence after the last lot gave out.

26

Sharon. Don't you like pop, Mrs B.?

Mrs Burroughs. I can live without it, love.

Philip. There won't be any more pop now, will there?

Sharon. 'Course there will. There are plenty of tapes and records around, just waiting to be picked up.

Philip. Yes, but there won't be anything new, will there? It'll all be old. We'll have heard it all before.

Sharon. We'll have to make our own. How are you on the guitar, Philip?

Philip. Rotten. But I can swing my hips. *(He does so)* Hey, I can play the mouth-organ.

Gillian. You'll have to practise, Phil.

Mrs Burroughs. Wait till we get outside, Philip.

(Alan and John come in)

Alan. Did I hear pop?

Sharon. Oh, here's the professor. He's like you, Mrs B., he prefers classical music.

Mrs Burroughs. Oh, I don't like classical music, love. I like the oldies.

Philip. Join the queue, you two. The bathroom's occupied by the ladies.

Sharon. Is it? Oh, good. I'll go in. *(She goes out)*

Gillian *(Rising)*. I may as well use the bathroom now. Then I'm not holding up the queue.

John. Is Tracy up yet?

Gillian. Not yet. Shall I call her?

John. I'll get her out. *(He crosses the room as Gillian goes out)*

John *(Shouting through the partly-open door)*. Come on, Tracy. Wakey, wakey. Rise and shine, the morning's fine. The sun's scorching your eyes out.

(Dr Ainsworth enters)

Dr Ainsworth. Where on earth did you learn that, John?

John. That's the way my dad used to get me up for school. I used to bury my head under the bedclothes and curse him. Still ... I wouldn't mind ... you know, hearing it again.

(Tracy comes in with a towel and crosses towards the bathroom)

Tracy *(To* **John***)*. What's all the rush? I've been up for hours. How could anybody sleep through all this racket?

*(***Tracy** *goes into the bathroom.* **Susan** *and* **Lynda** *come in.)*

Lynda *(Sweetly)*. Still waiting, Philip, dear?
Philip. For you, darling, I'll wait for ever.
Lynda. You may have to.

(She crosses to the dormitory)

Susan. Have they finished with the generators yet, Mrs B.?
Mrs Burroughs. Not yet, love, but they shouldn't be long. Let's go and make a start.

*(***Mrs Burroughs** *and* **Susan** *go into the kitchen)*

Alan. Who won't be long?
Philip. Mr Burroughs and Mr Boyle. They've gone outside to fix the generator.
Dr Ainsworth. We're all present or accounted for, except Terry. Where is he? I heard him stirring ages ago.

(There is a pause)

Alan. Don't you ever sleep, Doctor?
Dr Ainsworth. At my age, Alan, I sleep lightly. And I notice things ... like changes in the atmosphere. What's the mystery?
John. I haven't seen him.
Dr Ainsworth. Has he gone up top?
Alan. We don't really know.
Philip. You may as well tell the doctor. Mrs B.'s found out and she didn't throw a fit.
Alan. He did speak of going down to the village.
Philip. And it's pretty certain he has.
Dr Ainsworth. Well, I don't suppose it's the end of the world at this stage. He's not going to come to much harm, providing he doesn't stay too long.
Alan. He doesn't spend too long. Last time he was only ...
Dr Ainsworth. Last time? You mean he's been out before?

Alan. Yes.
Dr Ainsworth. How often?
John. Just once. About a week ago.

(Gillian, Sharon and Tracy enter, and cross to the dormitory)

Tracy. All right, Philip, it's your turn now.
Dr Ainsworth. You boys go in. I can wait.

(Alan, John and Philip go into the bathroom. There is a pause while Dr Ainsworth studies the map. Mrs Burroughs comes in and begins to lay the tables for breakfast.)

Mrs Burroughs. Good morning, Jim. You must have slept well. You're last up.
Dr Ainsworth. I never sleep well, Mary. I simply sleep enough for a man of my age. I've been aware of people creeping out of that dormitory ever since young Terry sneaked off and that must have been six o'clock.
Mrs Burroughs. You've heard then?
Dr Ainsworth. I gather he's off down the village again. Here, let me help you.

(He begins to set cutlery on the tables)

Mrs Burroughs. You don't think it's important?
Dr Ainsworth. I'm surprised it hasn't happened before.
Mrs Burroughs. And you don't think it will have harmed Terry?
Dr Ainsworth. We've all got to go up top sometime, Mary. And soon. We shall have to live with the danger of radiation blowing in on adverse winds. God knows what physical effect it will have on us in the long run. All that depends on luck, where we settle, where the winds blow, how much it rains, how quickly the radiation dies.
Mrs Burroughs. You're not very optimistic, Jim.
Dr Ainsworth. I've no reason to be, Mary. It's touch and go for the human race. You and I, Mary, we're not going to live as long as we hoped. And these youngsters, I doubt if they'll reach their threescore years and ten. But the next generation, Gillian's baby, they may attain something like normality, unless ...
Mrs Burroughs. Well?

29

Dr Ainsworth. I was just going to say, unless there's some imponderable, something that hasn't been observed or considered about radiation. Something that alters the genes, causes mutation, kills us off maybe. We don't know, Mary.

Mrs Burroughs. Oh, Jim! Change the subject. Try to think of something cheerful.

Dr Ainsworth. You asked for my considered opinion, Mary.

(Adam and Ted come in, removing their helmets)

Mrs Burroughs. Adam, you're back.

Burroughs. You weren't expecting anyone else were you, Mary?

Mrs Burroughs. Of course not, except . . .

Burroughs. Except who?

Dr Ainsworth. She probably means young Terry. He's apparently taken a trip to the village.

Mrs Burroughs. But he's not going to come to any harm. Jim admits as much. So we're not going to have a scene, are we Adam?

Burroughs. Haven't I been telling you for weeks, Mary, that it's safe to go out for short periods without a suit? Now she tells me. And here we've been sweating over that generator in these heavy suits! Women!

Mrs Burroughs. Can we start breakfast?

Boyle. Any time you like, Mrs B.

(Mrs Burroughs goes into the kitchen)

Burroughs. It seems a pointless exercise, Ted, but we may as well get under the showers. *(To Dr Ainsworth)* Is there anyone in there?

Dr Ainsworth. Some of the boys. They shouldn't be long.

Burroughs. As a matter of interest, Jim, just pass the geiger counter over us.

Dr Ainsworth. I'll get it. It's in my bag.

(He goes into the dormitory)

Boyle. Do you think we're clean, Adam?

Burroughs. The readings on the surface geiger counter suggest we ought to be. I'd just like to make sure. We need to be as near 100 per cent sure as possible, before we make a dash for Wales or the Lakes.

(Dr Ainsworth returns with his medical bag which he places on the radio table. He takes from it a small geiger counter which he passes over Burroughs and Boyle.)

Dr Ainsworth. Are you thinking of making a dash for it, Adam?

Burroughs. I was on to the Welsh group this morning, Jim. Their surveys show that the area's habitable. Question is, how do we get there? It would have to be by sea because of the intense radiation belt. Mary's pressing for the Lake District. Taking a chance on it's being clear.

Dr Ainsworth. Well, you two seem to be clear. *(He replaces the geiger counter in his bag)* I don't see any sense in showering off. Dump your gear and we'll have some breakfast.

(John and Alan enter)

John. Did I hear breakfast?

Dr Ainsworth. Shouldn't be long. Especially if you two give a hand in the kitchen.

John *(Crossing)*. I don't see why we have to do the housework with all these girls around.

Alan *(Also crossing)*. It's the new world, John. Get used to it.

Boyle. Let's get out of these suits. They're too hot.

(He goes out)

Burroughs. I'm with you there, Ted. I lose pounds in one of these.

(He follows)

Dr Ainsworth. I may as well join you. I haven't washed yet.

(He also follows. Alan and John return with cups, bread and butter, etc. and complete laying the table.)

John. Time Terry was back. He said he'd be back before anyone was stirring.

Alan. I hope nothing's happened to him.

John. What could?

Alan. Nothing I suppose, except an accident and that's not likely.

John. Do you think he'll have had it when Adam sees him?
Alan. No. Doc Ainsworth took it calmly enough.

(**Lynda** *comes in and goes to sit at the table*)

Lynda. Breakfast?
Alan. Workers first.
Lynda. I worked yesterday. Who do you think baked that bread?
Alan. You didn't!
John. She did. I saw her.

(**Sharon** *and* **Tracy** *come in and move to sit at the tables*)

Lynda. I thought I'd better learn how it's done.
Sharon. I'm going to start.

(*She takes a piece of bread and begins to eat it*)

Lynda. What's it like?
Sharon. Fine. Susan couldn't have done better.
Tracy (*Taking a piece*). I'll join you.

(**Burroughs**, **Boyle** *and* **Dr Ainsworth** *stroll in.* **Boyle** *goes to the table.* **Dr Ainsworth** *and* **Burroughs** *linger by the map.*)

Boyle. Have we started?
Alan. Some of the pigs couldn't wait to get to the trough.
Sharon. Charming!
Boyle (*Taking bread*). I'll join the pigs. I'm hungry.

(*The door bursts open and* **Terry** *is precipitated into the room at gunpoint by the* **Colonel**. **Two soldiers** *deploy to right and left. There is an 'alien' look about the intruders and their menace is immediate and overpowering. Their features are European in cast, but Mongoloid in colouring. The combat uniforms and 'crash' helmets might indicate spacemen, or air-crew, or perhaps riot police. Their guns have a technologically advanced appearance. There are exclamations of surprise and screams from the assembled group.* **Mrs Burroughs** *and* **Susan** *appear at the kitchen door.*)

32

Colonel *(In accented but correct English)*. This bunker is under military law. I formally take possession of it in the name of the Federation. (

Scene 2

Half-an-hour later. The **Colonel** is finishing his meal at the head of one of the tables. Most of the company have finished breakfast and are sitting away from the tables. One **soldier** still eats, the **other soldier** stands guard at the door.

Colonel. That was very good. Now, all I need is a cigarette and a good long sleep. *(He stretches and yawns)*

Philip. It's only half-past nine.

Colonel. We have been on duty for several days, boy, and will sleep when we can. *(To the company at large)* Cigarettes? No?

Burroughs *(Shortly)*. No. We don't smoke because of the air supply. And anyway the cigarettes up top will be contaminated.

Colonel. I think not, Mr ... er ...

Burroughs. Burroughs.

Colonel. Mr Burroughs. I cannot believe that our bombs would contaminate your supplies to that extent. That young man *(Pointing to* **Terry***)* was wandering around in the open air, yet large areas of my homeland are a radioactive desert.

Burroughs. And so are large areas of Britain. We happen to be lucky, as I presume you were.

Colonel. We were lucky, but not, I think, as lucky as you.

*(***Burroughs*** has risen and wandered over to the radio)*

Colonel. Mr Burroughs, you would not, I hope, be so foolish as to try to use that radio.

Burroughs. No.

Colonel. I was going to explain to you, Mr Burroughs, to all of you, why you are to be considered lucky.

Terry *(Sitting apart with* **Gillian***)*. Our luck's just turned. If I hadn't been down the village, you might not have caught us.

Colonel. You are mistaken, young man. We knew exactly where you were. Also the location of other groups. We have monitored your radio transmissions for many months. So you must not blame

33

yourself. You forgot that we are still at war, a war of unprovoked aggression against the Federation.

Boyle. We don't know who started it. We're unimportant civilians who happened to survive. For all we know, you may have started it. It –

Colonel. That is impossible.

Dr Ainsworth. It's history anyway. Let's get back to the present. Mr Boyle has just said that we're unimportant civilians, and so we are. Why should you people be interested in us?

Colonel. A good question, sir. And one that I was coming to when I spoke of your luck.

Burroughs. And why are we so lucky, apart from surviving?

Colonel. Because, Mr Burroughs, *(He spreads his hands)* you have women.

Mrs Burroughs. Women!

Colonel. Exactly, Madame. You have five young women, all capable of bearing children.

Mrs Burroughs. But they're only girls. Schoolchildren.

Colonel *(Indicating* **Gillian***).* I observe that English schoolchildren are capable of bearing children.

Burroughs. Good God, man! You mean you've come all this way for the girls?

Colonel. Precisely.

(Consternation in the company)

Dr Ainsworth. And you mean to take them?

Colonel. Exactly.

Boyle. But you can't. It's … it's inhuman. It's against international law. As civilians we have rights.

Colonel. It is the fortune of war, my friend. If you wish to protest, you can take your case to the International Court … if you can find it.

Burroughs. Have you no women of your own?

Colonel. Unfortunately not, Mr Burroughs. Not of a suitable age. No doubt there are some areas where women survive, but we are not in contact with them. And you will understand that it would be impossible for us to search a large country. We prefer to take from our enemies.

Terry. You're not taking them. We won't let you.

Colonel *(Patting his gun).* You have no option, young man. As I said, it is the fortune of war. We have the guns. We give the orders.

Terry *(Starting up).* I won't let you take Gillian. She's mine.

34

Colonel. Ah! The anxious father, hey? You do not need to fear for her safety or her comfort. Your five girls here will be the future mothers of our citizens and as such will be honoured.

Lynda. But we're English. We're not like you at all.

Colonel. Your children will be like us. That is enough.

Terry *(Advancing)*. Gillian's baby is English and that's the way it stays.

Colonel *(Drawing his gun)*. Do not advance any further, or I may be obliged to shoot you.

Gillian *(In panic)*. Do as he says, Terry. Please.

*(**Terry** allows himself to be pulled back to his seat)*

Colonel. I am glad you are being reasonable.

Burroughs. There's no reason in this situation. You can't uproot children from their country and use them as brood mares. Have you no feelings, man?

Colonel. I have a feeling for my homeland, Mr Burroughs. I wish to see it recover from the devastation caused by the powers that are hostile to us. I wish to see it great again. I wish to see it as a universal guiding force. As the only guiding force.

Burroughs. And the rest of the world can go hang?

Colonel. The rest of you can die out, Mr Burroughs. We have no desire to harm you.

Dr Ainsworth. And, of course, we will die out without young women, won't we?

Colonel. Exactly.

Dr Ainsworth. And you have other raids planned on other groups?

Colonel. You are the first. There are only a few others with suitable women. When we have visited them we shall leave you all in peace.

Mrs Burroughs. To die.

Colonel. It is the fate of all of us to die sometime, Madame.

Boyle. It's a crazy plan, this idea of dominating the world. Do you think you can capture every woman in England, let alone the world?

Colonel. We do not expect 100 per cent success. But the Federation will be the dominant power. It is historically inevitable.

Burroughs. Man, you're mad to think of power politics in a world catastrophe like this.

Colonel *(Coldly)*. We are not mad, Mr Burroughs. We see the situation clearly. We intend to see that what emerges is a society to our liking. *(Rising)* And now, if you will excuse me, we must rest.

The soldier here will remain on guard for one hour. Then he will be relieved for one hour. At the end of that time the young women must be ready to leave. Our helicopter is a large one, but as there will be other passengers there will be no room for baggage, only small items of a personal nature. Everything necessary will be provided for them in their new home. *(To* **Burroughs***)* Do not be so foolish as to attempt an attack on the sentry. He has orders to shoot at the least threatening move. Be sensible and you will come to no harm. *(To the* **Sergeant** *who is still eating)* Turmi, ze soluti. [*Come, we will sleep.*] *(To the* **Sentry***)* Pre dolantor. [*Be vigilant.*]

(He moves to the dormitory door followed by the **Sergeant***)*

You have two hours, remember, to say your goodbyes.

(He and the **Sergeant** *exit. There is a pause. When the dialogue begins again it has a muted quality.)*

Terry. What are we going to do? We can't let them get away with this.
Burroughs. For the moment, we do nothing. Just sit and chat, or put in some hard thinking.
Boyle. We could rush that sentry. He couldn't get everybody.
Burroughs. We don't want any shooting. We don't want any unusual noise at all. It would bring out the other two and we'd be trapped. Just keep talking normally, about anything at all. We've got to keep things natural. Let the two in there get to sleep.
Lynda. Talk naturally! When I'm about to be married off to one of those things!
Philip. You prefer me, darling?
Lynda. You know, I think I do.
Philip. Victory!
Boyle. Keep your voice down, Philip.
Philip. Sorry.
Alan. You were right, Mr Burroughs, when you said this fellow was mad. Whoever heard of conquering the world by capturing all the women?
Burroughs. It's a new line in conquest, certainly.
Dr Ainsworth. It's a load of fanatical eyewash. He couldn't possibly hope to capture all the women in Europe, let alone America and the rest of the world. This is just the Sabine Women all over again.
Tracy. Who were they, Doctor Ainsworth?

36

Dr Ainsworth. A group of women from way back who were in your position, Tracy.

Sharon. Did they get out of it, Doc?

Dr Ainsworth. I'm afraid not, Sharon. But we'll do our best for you.

Boyle. It's a reversion to the primitive, isn't it? This notion of one tribe making off with the women of another tribe.

Dr Ainsworth. That's the way I see it, Ted. I think this Colonel is in command of a group of men who haven't seen a woman for eight months. So he goes off raiding the first likely group he hears of. Then he disguises what he's doing by calling it 'a blow for the Federation' or some such nonsense.

Burroughs. Maybe you're right, Jim. But the result's the same to us whether he's sincere or not.

John. Do you think there was any truth in what he was saying? About us starting the war?

Burroughs. We're never likely to know, John. Not for sure. You can be pretty sure that the whole damnable business was an accident or the work of a madman.

Dr Ainsworth. We've been on a knife-edge since Hiroshima, Adam. I always thought it was bound to happen sometime. I just hoped it wouldn't be in my lifetime.

John. If you thought that, why didn't you do something about it?

Alan. After all it's you older ones who got us into this mess.

Burroughs. We older ones as you call us, Alan, hadn't any say in the matter. Oh, we could vote at election-time and some people demonstrated pretty vigorously. My own son, when he was a student, spent half his time marching up and down with anti-Bomb posters. But it didn't affect the governments. They just went on building bigger bombs and better means of delivery. And the protesters got discouraged and the war-scares fewer, and people, and maybe governments too, swept the whole messy business under the mat and tried to forget about it.

Mrs Burroughs. Let's get back to the present, Adam. What are we going to do?

Burroughs. We can talk now, I hope. They should be dozing off and I don't imagine that sentry has any idea what we're saying. He hasn't shown the least flicker of interest. Has anybody any ideas? Apart from rushing him, because that's out.

Boyle. Where's your gun?

Burroughs. It's back in that drawer under the radio, but we can't start a shooting match. And I'm not so sure I could even hit him.

Terry. Couldn't we distract him somehow and take him from behind?

Dr Ainsworth. It needs to be quieter than that. I know what would do it if we could work the trick.

Burroughs. What?

Dr Ainsworth. One of my special pills. He'd just go drowsy, feel on top of the world and quietly die. Question is, how do we get him to take one?

Mrs Burroughs. We could make a cup of tea and give him one. Will it dissolve in tea, Jim?

Dr Ainsworth. Yes, they're soluble.

Susan. Suppose he doesn't like tea?

Mrs Burroughs. He drank it at breakfast. They all did.

Tracy. What if he's not thirsty?

Terry. We've got to try it.

Boyle. He may not let us out of his sight to make the tea.

Burroughs. Try clearing the table, Mary. See if he objects to that. One of you girls give her a hand. He may let women out, but not the men.

(Mrs Burroughs begins clearing the table)

Tracy. I'll give you a hand, Mrs B. I'll be glad to get out of sight of his gun.

(She begins to help. The sentry eyes them watchfully, but makes no attempt to stop them.)

Dr Ainsworth. I have to get my bag.

Burroughs. You'd better wait till the table's cleared. That fellow might be suspicious of too much movement.

Dr Ainsworth. Yes, but he's suffering somewhat from fatigue, I think. That should help to dull his senses.

Boyle. How are we going to get the tablet in his cup?

Dr Ainsworth. Leave that to me. I'll pretend to take a headache tablet, but it really goes into a special cup. *(To* **Mrs Burroughs***, who has returned)* Leave one cup with a spoon in it, Mary. Everybody clear on that? You leave the cup with the spoon strictly alone. See that Tracy knows, Mary. We hand them round, then give him one as

an afterthought. If he sees us drinking he shouldn't be
suspicious.

Mrs Burroughs. I'll hand them round, including the sentry's.

Burroughs. Mary, I think it would ...

Mrs Burroughs. No, Adam. It's safer if I do it. As you said, he'll be less
suspicious of a woman.

Dr Ainsworth. She's right, Adam. If *you* don't mind, Mary?

Mrs Burroughs. No, Jim. I'll do it. *(She returns to the kitchen)*

Burroughs. I don't like it, Jim. I'd rather it was you or me.

Dr Ainsworth. It makes sense, Adam. We can't afford to fail. *(To the
company)* I'm going to my bag now. I don't want anybody
watching me. Talk naturally, even if it's nonsense. But keep
talking.

(He begins to move to the radio-table)

Susan. I never could talk when I had to. Never knew what to say.

Sharon. I know what you mean. Like having to stand up in class and
give a speech.

Lynda. Making speeches never bothered me.

Philip. You never have been short of something to say, have you, Lynda?

Lynda. I could always find the right words for somebody like you, mate.

*(During the dialogue **Dr Ainsworth** has reached his bag, opened it
and produced a phial of white tablets. The **Sentry** follows his
movements with his gun suspiciously. **Dr Ainsworth** looks up to
see the pointed gun and reacts with mock astonishment, pointing
to the tablets and then to his head.)*

Dr Ainsworth. Tablets. Headache.

*(The **Sentry** relaxes as **Dr Ainsworth** moves away from his bag)*

Burroughs. Keep talking, if only about the weather.

John. We haven't seen much of that recently, have we?

Gillian *(Nervously)*. How was it up top, Terry? Was it raining, cold?
What?

Terry. The sun was shining. It was a warm, spring day. The trees were
in bud, so there's life still going on.

(Dr Ainsworth has moved back to the group and has shaken out a tablet from the bottle and placed it on the table. The bottle goes into his pocket.)

Dr Ainsworth. There's the pill. On the table. Don't look at it. Just leave it to me. For God's sake don't take the cup with the spoon in it.

(Mrs Burroughs and Tracy come in with a tray of cups with the tea ready poured. One cup has the spoon in it. The tray is placed on the table near Dr Ainsworth.)

Dr Ainsworth. Oh, good. The tea. Now I can have my tablet.

(He quickly drops the tablet into the cup with the spoon and stirs vigorously. He then takes another cup and mimes taking a tablet. People near the tray take cups. The remaining cups are handed round by Mrs Burroughs.)

Burroughs. If you can't drink without your hand shaking, leave it for the moment. Those who can drink look as if you're enjoying it.

Sharon. My mouth's dry with excitement. I need a drink.

Alan. It's nerve-racking. Has he taken a cup?

Terry. Not yet.

Dr Ainsworth. Keep your eyes on your own cup or on somebody else. And keep the talk going.

Gillian. I hope it works. I want to get out of here, fast.

Terry. How are we going to travel, Mr Burroughs? And where to?

Burroughs. We'll use your old school minibus. It's still where Tom parked it that night he came back.

Alan. Will it go?

Burroughs. I've checked it a couple of times. Last time about a week ago. The engine's O.K.

John. I hope it starts. We can't afford to waste time fiddling with an engine.

Burroughs. It's a bit low on petrol, but there's enough to get us clear.

Tracy. What happens if it doesn't start?

Burroughs. We start walking. North. Till we pick up some other transport.

Mrs Burroughs *(To the soldier)*. Tea? A cup of tea?

Soldier. Prosiva. [*Thank you.*]

Mrs Burroughs *(With the spoon poised over the sugar bowl)*. Sugar?
Soldier. Nova. [*No.*]

*(He takes the cup with his left hand, keeping a wary eye on the
others. He then sits on the top step, his gun resting across his knee,
and drinks.* **Mrs Burroughs** *sits.)*

Burroughs. If we're forced to walk, we keep off the roads for a while.
Keep to the hedges and the trees. Use what cover there is, in case
that helicopter of theirs gets airborne.
Terry. And if the bus works, where do we head for?
Burroughs. The Lakes. In case there's any slip-up and we have to
separate, we'd better make a rendezvous. Let's say Windermere.
The landing stage at Bowness. That clear, everybody? The Bowness
landing stage on Windermere.
Philip. What's happening? I'm dying to look round.
Mrs Burroughs. Nothing yet. He's taking his time.
Burroughs. Where exactly is he, Mary?
Mrs Burroughs. Sitting on the top step.
Dr Ainsworth. If he falls down the steps there's bound to be some noise.
We'd better be ready to catch him.
Burroughs. Warn us, Mary, as soon as he begins to keel over.
Boyle. How long does the pill take, Doc?
Dr Ainsworth. Supposed to be about a minute, but he's taking his time
drinking it.
Mrs Burroughs. He's drinking it off now. Shall I take the cup from him?
Burroughs. See if he puts it down first.
Mrs Burroughs. Yes, he has. He's put it on the step.
Lynda. This waiting! I feel like screaming.
Boyle. Keep control of yourself, Lynda. Everything depends on our
keeping things normal.
Mrs Burroughs. It's beginning to take effect, I think. His head's nodding.
Burroughs. Keep perfectly still everyone. Ted, you and I will go for him
when Mary gives the word.
Mrs Burroughs *(Urgently)*. Now. He's sliding down.

*(***Burroughs** *and* **Boyle** *move swiftly to the steps and control the
sliding body.* **Boyle** *grabs the gun. They ease the body clear of the
steps.)*

41

Boyle. I hope I know how to work this thing. *(He covers the dormitory door)*

Burroughs. Girls first. Quietly. Mary, you take them to the bus. Can one of you boys start the engine?

Terry. I can.

Burroughs. You take Gillian, Terry, and get the bus started. Don't use too much choke.

(The girls and **Terry** *are moving out quietly, shepherded by* **Mrs Burroughs***)*

The boys follow when the steps are clear. Keep it quiet.

*(***Burroughs** *goes to the drawer of the radio table and takes out the revolver seen in Act One)*

Dr Ainsworth *(Moving to the radio table)*. I'd better have my bag.

Burroughs. You see the boys out, Jim. Ted and I will wait until you've had time to get to the bus. If we don't appear in what seems to you a reasonable time, move off.

Dr Ainsworth. Without you?

Burroughs. If necessary. Get moving, Jim.

*(***Dr Ainsworth** *follows the boys out.* **Burroughs** *and* **Boyle** *are left covering the door.)*

Boyle. It sounds like a herd of elephants tramping out.

Burroughs. Not really. Just seems that way.

Boyle. I hope that bus starts. It was never noted for its reliability.

Burroughs. If it gets us clear of the district, that's all we need. We can always hole up somewhere and move on when the coast's clear.

Boyle. I see you've got your old gun. Remember when we had our little disagreement?

Burroughs. Yes. I'm glad you all stayed, Ted. It's made the whole exercise seem worthwhile. Having the youngsters to look after and so on. I don't know about you, but it gave me a stake in the future.

Boyle. I know what you mean, Adam.

Burroughs. Of course, you're still young, Ted. It's your future as well.

Boyle. Not a very bright one. Still, better than having no future at all.

Burroughs. That's the way it would have been without the girls.

(There is a slight pause) I think that's enough, Ted. We'll move out. You go first.

*(**Boyle** crosses to the steps and exits cautiously, followed by **Burroughs**. There is a long pause. The the dormitory door opens and the **Colonel** enters. The emptiness of the room shocks him into wakefulness. He sees the **soldier's** body, draws his gun and crosses to the steps. He checks the man's heart, then goes swiftly back to the door, shouting through it.)*

Colonel. Saporela! Turmi fedaste! [*Sergeant! Come quickly!*]

*(He throws open the other doors and takes a hasty look inside. The **Sergeant** runs in.)*

Che vegati. Ulmar rateba. Turmi. [*They have escaped. Ulmar is dead. Follow me.*]

*(He rushes out, followed by the **Sergeant**)*

43

ACT THREE

Scene 1

An hour later. A hill-top. One corner of a bungalow is visible. The open
door and damaged windows suggest that it is derelict. The roses climbing
the trellis around the door are beginning to show leaves, but are not yet
in flower. Two rustic benches stand in the garden, flanking the path.
Two tubs, with shrubs, stand one on each side of the door. Upstage,
steps lead to an entrance to another part of the garden, bordered by
green hedging. Beyond the hedge is a stunted apple tree.
At the rise of the curtain the stage is empty. Voices are heard off.

Dr Ainsworth *(Off)*. It's as good a place as we're likely to find.
Gillian *(Off)*. I'm sorry to be such a trouble.
Dr Ainsworth *(Off)*. It's no trouble, my dear. I'm used to it ... or I was.

> *(Dr Ainsworth enters followed by Gillian who is supported by
> Terry. She is in the first stages of labour. Terry leads her to the
> first bench where they both sit, holding hands.)*

Dr Ainsworth. Bring her over here, Terry and let her sit down.
Gillian. I'm sorry, Doc.
Terry. Don't keep apologising, love. It's not your fault.
Dr Ainsworth. No, it's that baby. The excitement must have been too
    much for him.
Gillian. Her. It's going to be a girl.
Dr Ainsworth. Him or her. It's a queer world to be born into.

> *(Mrs Burroughs enters, followed by the girls)*

Mary, I'm going to take a look inside. If it's clear, I want you and
the girls to get a bed ready. Get a fire going too. We'll need some
hot water.
Mrs Burroughs. When you're ready, Jim.

44

(Doctor Ainsworth goes into the house)

Sharon. What does he mean 'If it's clear'?
Mrs Burroughs. The previous owners may still be there, Sharon.
Sharon. Oh! You mean . . . dead?
Mrs Burroughs. They're not likely to be alive after all this.
Lynda. It's gruesome, isn't it?
Tracy. It'll be like this wherever we go, won't it? Dead bodies all over
     the place. Skeletons!
Terry. For God's sake, talk about something more cheerful. You'll upset
     Gill.
Tracy. Sorry, Gill.
Gillian. That's all right, Tracy. It doesn't upset me. I've other things on
     my mind.
Mrs Burroughs. That's right, love. You concentrate on essentials. We'll
     soon have you into bed.

(Dr Ainsworth appears at the door)

Dr Ainsworth. You can come in, Mary. There's nothing to bother us
     here.
Mrs Burroughs *(Crossing)*. I expect they left in a hurry.
Dr Ainsworth. You're right. They didn't have time to wash the pots.
Mrs Burroughs. Come on, girls. Let's get busy.

(The girls, except Gillian, follow Mrs Burroughs into the house)

Dr Ainsworth. You all right, Gillian? No more pains?
Gillian. I haven't had a pain since we stopped.
Dr Ainsworth. If you need me, send Terry.

(Burroughs comes on followed by John and Philip)

Burroughs. Will the house do, Jim?
Dr Ainsworth. Couldn't be better, Adam. No mess to clear up. They
     seem to have had central heating, but there's one open fireplace.
     We'll need wood though. You lads collect some, will you?
     Anything that will burn. Fencing might be easiest. There's a shed
     at the back. Break that up if you can't find anything else.
Philip. Come on, the demolition men.

(Philip marches up the steps into the upper garden, followed by John)

Burroughs. Do you need any help inside, Jim? I'm willing, but not very skilled, if you know what I mean.

Dr Ainsworth. I don't need an engineer to help me deliver a baby, Adam. Have you nothing else to keep you busy?

Burroughs. No. Ted and Alan are filling up with petrol. We managed to open up the tanks and found a semi-rotary pump. They can cope on their own.

Dr Ainsworth. You'd better just sit it out then, Adam. I'll go and see how Mary and the girls are coping.

(He goes into the house. Burroughs sits in the empty rustic seat.)

Gillian. Mr Burroughs.

Burroughs. Um?

Gillian. You're sort of . . . in charge of us all, aren't you?

Burroughs. You could say that, Gillian. Though at the moment I think Dr Ainsworth is more the Captain of the ship than I am.

Terry. Yes, but up to now you've been the boss, like Noah in the Ark.

Burroughs. Quite an appropriate comparison, Terry. Adam's Ark, eh?

Gillian. Well, we were wondering . . .

(She is interrupted by John and Philip returning with wood for the fire.)

Philip. Make way for the woodcutters.

John. Let's start on the shed. It'll be quicker than looking for dead stuff.

(They go into the house)

Burroughs. You were saying, Gillian?

Gillian. Terry and I were wondering if you could . . . well . . . marry us.

Burroughs. Marry you! I hardly think I'm qualified to . . .

Terry. But you are really. Like the captain of a ship. You've power to do anything you want.

Burroughs. I wouldn't know the words.

Gillian. Just make them up, Mr Burroughs.

46

(Mrs Burroughs appears at the door)

Mrs Burroughs. We're ready if you are, Gillian.
Gillian. Not just yet, Mrs B.
Mrs Burroughs. Twenty minutes ago, you couldn't wait.
Burroughs. These two young people have decided they want to be married, Mary. And they want me to perform the ceremony.
Mrs Burroughs. Well . . . all I can say is . . . you've left it rather late.
Gillian. We never thought of it before, Mrs B.
Terry. And we wanted everything to be . . . well . . . legal.
Mrs Burroughs. Do you remember the words, Adam?
Gillian. He's going to make them up.
Mrs Burroughs. Shall I call the others? We haven't much of a congregation.
Gillian. I'd rather it was . . . quiet.
Burroughs *(Approaching them)*. Well, I'll do my best. Can you stand, Gillian? Or shall I marry you sitting down?
Gillian. I'll stand.

(She struggles to her feet, helped by Terry, *but has a spasm of pain)*

Terry. Are you sure you're all right, love?
Gillian. Yes, I think so. It won't take long will it, Mr Burroughs?
Burroughs. It'll be the shortest wedding on record, Gillian. Are you ready?

(Gillian nods assent)

Do you, Terry, take Gillian to be your lawful wife?
Terry. I do.
Burroughs. Do you, Gillian, take Terry to be your lawful husband?
Gillian. I do.
Burroughs. By whatever power God or the Fates have granted me, I pronounce you man and wife.

(Terry shyly kisses Gillian. Mrs Burroughs *kisses them both.)*

Mrs Burroughs. God bless you. Both of you. I hope you'll be very happy, in spite of everything.

*(*Burroughs *shakes* Terry's *hand and kisses* Gillian*)*

Burroughs. Well, it may not read like that in the book, but it's as legal
as I can make it. I hope the baby brings you much happiness.
Mrs Burroughs. The baby! Come on, Gillian. It's time we had you in bed.

(She begins to lead Gillian *off,* Terry *following)*

You stay here, young man. This is women's business.
Terry. I'd rather come in, Mrs B.
Mrs Burroughs. We'll see what the doctor says. Come on then.

*(*Gillian, Terry *and* Mrs Burroughs *go into the house. There is a
slight pause while* Burroughs *sits meditatively on the seat.* Boyle
and Alan *come on.)*

Boyle. We've topped up the old bus. Filled some spare cans as well.
Burroughs. Good.
Alan. Where is everybody?
Burroughs. They're in the house, on urgent business connected with a
baby.
Alan. All of them?
Burroughs. Philip and John are collecting wood. Breaking up the shed I
gather. It must be a bit wet from the amount of smoke going up.

(He looks at the roof of the bungalow)

Alan. Shall I go and help?
Burroughs. No, they'll manage. Sit down and wait. There's nothing to
do now but wait.

(Alan *and* Boyle *sit)*

Boyle. We parked the bus under the trees, a hundred yards back.
Burroughs. Good idea. You're thinking of that enemy helicopter, I
suppose.
Boyle. Yes.
Burroughs. I've been thinking of that ever since we made a break for it.
Alan. You mean we should have smashed it?

48

Burroughs. Or made sure the Colonel and the Sergeant weren't able to follow us.

Boyle. We should have killed them as well, you mean?

Burroughs. If necessary. It would have been enough to take their guns, though. Render them harmless.

Boyle. I'm glad we didn't try. I didn't feel very confident handling a tommy-gun.

Burroughs. We'll just have to hope they're still sleeping. Or that they can't pick up our trail. Where's our gun, by the way?

Boyle. I left it in the cab. I didn't think . . .

Burroughs. It's safer there. We don't want young Philip playing with it. Or Alan for that matter.

Alan. I haven't played cops and robbers for some time, Mr Burroughs. Real guns like that frighten me off.

Burroughs. Noisy things. Anyway, I've still got mine. *(He takes it out)* Though I don't know whether I could hit the side of the house. I wasn't very accurate when I practiced with it.

(He puts the revolver away as **Sharon**, **Lynda** *and* **Tracy** *come from the house.* **Sharon** *is still carrying her cassette recorder.)*

Sharon. We've been sent out to join you.

Tracy. No further use for our services.

Sharon. Mrs B.'s kept Susan, though.

Lynda. Well, we know when we're not wanted.

Boyle. Could it be, Lynda, that Susan is just that bit more competent that the rest of you?

Lynda. Oh, we know that. She was always teacher's pet.

Sharon. We have other qualities, don't we, Alan?

Alan. You may have. Can't say that I've noticed them particularly.

Tracy. Hey, Mr Burroughs. Mrs B. said you'd married Gill and Terry.

Burroughs. I did.

Sharon. She didn't have a ring, though.

Burroughs. The right words have been said, Sharon, so it's as legal as it can be. Ring or no ring.

Lynda. They say weddings go in threes, don't they?

Boyle. Do they, Lynda?

Lynda. Well, lots of things do. Why not weddings?

Sharon. I wonder who'll be next. Any ideas, Alan?

Alan. You know, I never can make out whether she's joking or serious.

Burroughs. Oh, serious, Alan. Women don't joke about marriage.

   (Philip and John come on)

Philip. Still on about weddings? Hey, what about old Terry losing his
   liberty? Another bachelor bit the dust!
Boyle. Don't be too confident, Philip. The girls say that weddings go in
   threes.
Philip *(Going down on one knee in a mock formal proposal)*. Lynda,
   darling. Will you marry me?
Lynda. Yes, I will.
Philip *(Jumping up in alarm)*. You will!
Lynda. You're as daft as a brush, but I reckon I can ~~knock~~ some sense
   into you.
Philip. But I was only kidding. *(Pleading)* Lynda, you know we only
   make a joke of it.
John. Another bachelor bit the dust!

   *(They are shocked into silence for a moment by Gillian's scream
   from the house)*

Tracy. It's started, then.
Burroughs. Does that tape recorder of yours still work, Sharon?
Sharon. Yes, Mr Burroughs.
Burroughs. Would you like to play something for us, Sharon?
Sharon. I didn't think you were a pop fan, Mr Burroughs.
Burroughs. Well, just this once, I think I'd like to hear you play it.

   *(Sharon turns on a flood of pop. The girls dance to it in a half-
   hearted way. Burroughs and Boyle drift away to avoid the
   immediate impact of the noise. They talk with difficulty above
   the music.)*

Boyle. How long do these things take, Adam?
Burroughs *(Not hearing)*. What?
Boyle. How long does it take for a baby to be born?
Burroughs. I don't know, Ted.
Boyle. I presume we'll have to stay here several days. Until Gillian's fit
   enough to travel.
Burroughs. We could be stuck here for a week. Pity it had to be here.

Far better if we'd been in a town where things were handy. We'll
need food and bedding.

Boyle. Will it be edible?

Burroughs (Not hearing). What?

Boyle. The food. Canned stuff. Will it be fit to eat?

Burroughs. We'll have to risk it.

(Mrs Burroughs appears at the door, calling for less noise)

Mrs Burroughs. Turn it down.

(Sharon turns down the volume until Mrs Burroughs can be heard)

Mrs Burroughs. It's hardly the time for a pop festival.

Burroughs. My fault, Mary. I thought a bit of music might take our
minds off the ... situation.

Mrs Burroughs. It needn't be so loud. Keep it down, Sharon.

(She returns to the house)

Sharon. Should I turn it off, Mr Burroughs? Seems a bit heartless ...
dancing while Gill's.... you know.

Lynda. Gill won't be bothering. She'll have her mind on other things.

Burroughs. Keep it nice and low, Sharon. Just enough for us to be able
to talk without shouting our heads off.

Tracy. I wonder how long we'll have to wait.

Philip. I'm getting hungry. When do we eat?

Lynda. It's not two hours since you had your breakfast.

Philip. Seems longer than that.

Alan. How are we going to eat? There can't be much in the house.

Burroughs. We'll send a party into town to collect some food when the
baby's born. There's no point in going before. There'll be a long
shopping list for the baby as well as food. I want Mary to go along
for that.

Lynda. We're going to be like millionaires, though, aren't we? Anything
we want ... there for the asking. Clothes, jewellery, anything you
like to name.

Burroughs. Maybe we shan't have time to enjoy all those luxuries,
Lynda. Don't forget, we'll be farmers, growing our own food. We
can't live on tinned stuff for ever.

Tracy. I don't think I'm going to like our new world particularly.

Philip. Oh, cheer up. It's better than being dead.

(There is alarm as the **Colonel** *and his* **Sergeant** *appear rapidly and cover the party with their guns)*

Colonel. Remain where you are.

(He motions the **Sergeant** *to one side where he crouches, covering the party with his gun. The* **Colonel** *crosses to the house door. The music is switched off.)*

Who is in the house?

Burroughs. A baby is being born. The doctor and his wife are with the girl.

Colonel. And the gun? Where is the gun you took after killing my man?

Burroughs. It's in the bus. Up the road.

Colonel *(Relaxing).* Good. It would not be wise of you to begin a battle. You could expect no mercy after what you have done.

Burroughs. We were only trying to protect ourselves. You couldn't expect us to let the girls go without a fight.

Colonel. The fight is over and you have lost. You, as the leader, I hold responsible for the death of my man. I shall consider in time what is to be done with you.

Burroughs. I accept the responsibility. I would do the same again.

Colonel. Then you would be foolish. You cannot hope to evade the vigilance of the Federation. What kind of leader are you, I wonder? You gain a temporary advantage and then you send up smoke signals.

Burroughs. We needed hot water for the birth. We had to take a risk. Otherwise you wouldn't have found us so easily.

Colonel *(Approaching him).* Eventually we should have found you. You had only one escape route. That we knew. Somewhere, sometime, you would have betrayed your presence.

Burroughs *(Wearily).* All right. We'll accept for the moment, that you've won. What do you propose doing?

Colonel. The young women will be taken to our helicopter at once. Then we shall carry out the rest of our plan.

Burroughs. There's one girl who can't be moved. She's giving birth to her child.

52

Colonel. We will wait for the birth. Then we go.

(Terry dashes in, unaware of the Colonel's presence)

Terry. Hey! It's a girl!
Colonel. Good. She will be the first of our young citizens.
Terry. What!
Colonel. It is important that we have plenty of girl children. They will
    be the mothers of our new world.
Terry *(Furiously approaching the Colonel)*. You're not taking her.
    Neither the baby nor Gill. They're staying here with me.
Colonel *(Raising his gun)*. Stay where you are. If you approach further
    I will shoot.

*(Burroughs takes out his revolver and shoots the Colonel in the
back. Then he fires at and hits the Sergeant.)*

Scene 2

As in Act Three Scene 1. Four days later. At the rise of the curtain the
stage is empty. **Boyle** and **Alan** come on and cross to the house. **Boyle**
stays by the door. **Alan** goes in.

Boyle. Get your stuff, Alan. Mine's in the bus already.
Alan. Won't take a minute.

(He goes into the house)

Boyle *(Calling into the house)*. Come on, everybody. The carriage is
    waiting.

*(Philip appears, carrying a heavy bag. He is dressed casually, as are
all the young people.)*

Philip. Hello, Mr Boyle. Are we ready to move off?
Boyle. We are, Philip. We'd have been ready sooner if you'd been around
    to give a hand.
Philip. You've moved the helicopter on your own?
Boyle. Alan helped me. As a matter of fact, it was quite easy. It rolled

53

down the slope and conveniently tipped over into the ditch. We
didn't really need you. I just wondered where you'd disappeared
to.
Philip. I've been packing.

(He indicates the bag)

Boyle. What on earth have you got in there? The kitchen sink?
Philip. It's all the gear I brought back from town the other day. I needed
some fresh clothes after all those months in school uniform.
I didn't bring half as much as the girls.
Boyle. Get aboard then. I hope the bus will stand the weight.

*(***Philip** *moves to go out.* **Sharon**, **Lynda**, **Tracy** *and* **John** *enter
from the house with their luggage.)*

Philip. If it won't, we'll have to get another, won't we? There are plenty
left parked around.

(He goes out)

Lynda. What's he going on about now?
Boyle. I was wondering if the bus would take all this luggage you seem
to have accumulated in a very short space of time. Philip suggests
we find a bigger bus.
Lynda. I've got bags of stuff.
Boyle. So I see.
Sharon. We found a smashing boutique.
Boyle. Spare me the details. I can imagine. Get your luggage aboard ...
if you can carry it.

*(***Sharon** *and* **Lynda** *move off)*

Tracy *(To* **John***).* If some people were gentlemen, they might give a girl
a hand.
John. Come on, then. I can manage one for you.

(They move off. **Alan** *enters from the house, carrying a small grip.
He is followed by* **Dr Ainsworth***.)*

54

Alan. That didn't take long, did it? I haven't been grabbing everything in sight, like some I could mention.

(He goes off)

Dr Ainsworth. The others shouldn't be long, Ted. Mary's fussing over the baby like it was her own grandchild. Doesn't seem to think Gillian can handle it with any degree of safety.

Boyle. Why are new babies always 'it'?

Dr Ainsworth. I never stopped to think about it, Ted. I suppose it's because they all look alike.

Boyle. How much travelling can Gillian stand?

Dr Ainsworth. Oh, she'll stand the journey to the Lakes. Should be smooth going when we hit the motorway. Anyway, we can stop when we like. No need for panic now.

Boyle. I suppose not. It's a relief to have that gang off our tails.

Dr Ainsworth. Yes. Adam solved the problem very neatly. Though he doesn't see it like that.

Boyle. It bothers him?

Dr Ainsworth. Somewhat. Would it trouble your conscience, Ted?

Boyle. Perhaps. For a while anyway.

(Terry and Gillian come on from the house. Gillian carries the baby, Terry their luggage.)

Dr Ainsworth. Quite the young married couple. You could be off to Blackpool for your holidays.

Boyle. Have you decided on the name yet, Gillian?

Gillian. Margaret Mary. Margaret after my mother and Mary after Mrs B.

Terry. We were going to call her Mary Margaret but Gill decided it was better the other way round, so Mrs B. had to take second place.

Dr Ainsworth. Well, I don't expect she'll mind taking second place to your mother, Gillian.

Gillian. I've a lot to thank Mrs B. for. And you too, Doctor.

Dr Ainsworth. Oh, it was nothing, my dear. I must have delivered close on a thousand babies in my time and yours was one of the easiest, Gillian. We had more trouble with the father.

Terry. I wasn't as bad as all that. A bit nervous, maybe.

Dr Ainsworth. A case of acute neurosis. Prospective fathers are better off at home ... or in the pub.

(Susan appears carrying a small bag, and the baby's carry-cot)

Susan. Mrs B. says she won't be long. She's tidying up. Though why she bothers, I don't know. The owners aren't likely to be back.

Dr Ainsworth. Force of habit, Susan. Mary always was one for keeping the place tidy.

Boyle. Do you need any help, Terry?

Terry. No, I'll manage. Susan's bringing the carry-cot.

(Terry, Gillian and Susan move off)

Boyle. That bus is going to be bursting at the seams.

Dr Ainsworth. We'd better pick up a good car as soon as we can. Relieve the congestion.

Boyle. I'll go and see them packed in.

(He goes off)

Dr Ainsworth. Save me a seat. I'll join you in a moment.

(He turns back to the house and calls through the door)

Mary! Adam! We're ready to move off.

(He crosses and goes off. Mr and Mrs Burroughs come on from the house, carrying light luggage.)

Mrs Burroughs. I'm sure to have forgotten something, Adam.

Burroughs. If you have, love, we can pick it up somewhere on the way. There's no shortage of anything now, except people.

Mrs Burroughs. I suppose so. You know, Adam, I was wondering what to get Gillian for the baby and then I realised that presents don't mean anything any more. Whatever she needs for the baby she can just nip out to the shop and get.

Burroughs. You can always knit.

Mrs Burroughs. I never was much of a hand at knitting. Not like your mother. Do you remember the things she knitted for David? How grateful we were?

Burroughs. We were struggling in those days, love, weren't we? When I was just starting. Now we're back struggling. It's ironic, isn't it?

I go through thirty years of married life without harming a soul, so far as I can recall, and then in one day I poison one man and shoot two others.

Mrs Burroughs. You did right, Adam. And you didn't poison the other. I did. So we're both as guilty. It doesn't trouble my conscience, Adam.

Burroughs *(Moving to overlook the upper garden)*. Still, there are two men buried out there who would be alive now if I hadn't pulled the trigger. You see, Mary, from one point of view it doesn't much matter who survives and multiplies, providing somebody does.

Mrs Burroughs. Sometimes I lose my patience with you, Adam. It's quite obvious to me that it's better for the English to survive. We all look after our own. After all, those aliens were doing just that. I was surprised you and Ted didn't finish off the job in the bunker. We'd have been saved this latest scare. I'm only thankful we came out of it as well as we did. And so are all the others.

(Sharon comes on, crossing to the house)

Sharon. I forgot my tape-recorder. I know I can get another, but I thought I'd keep my own for sentimental reasons.

(She goes into the house)

Mrs Burroughs. Would you rather have Sharon and the rest in some communal baby factory?

Burroughs. No. I know you've logic on your side, Mary. It just doesn't feel right, that's all, to be starting a new life on the basis of murdering your enemies.

Mrs Burroughs. It was no murder, Adam. And anyway, what about all those millions they killed with their bombs, David among them?

Burroughs. We don't know for certain, love, about David. We probably won't ever know.

Mrs Burroughs. That's the worst of it, Adam. The not knowing. I could bear it better if I knew for certain he was dead. At the moment, I'm not disposed to be sentimental over three thugs who tried to wreck what future we might have. What you did was a perfectly justifiable defence of our own lives.

(Sharon returns from the house with her tape-recorder and crosses)

57

Sharon. Got it. You know, it's going to rain, I think. That's good, isn't it, Mr Burroughs? I remember Doc once saying the rain would wash the earth clean. Oh, Mr Boyle said to tell you we're all ready when you are.

(She goes)

Mrs Burroughs. It is looking black.
Burroughs. It's already raining down in the valley.

(A rainbow appears on the cyclorama)

Mrs Burroughs. A rainbow. First we've seen for a long time.
Burroughs. First rain we've had since we came up top.
Mrs Burroughs. Remember the Bible, Adam?
Burroughs. Not very well, love. Which part?
Mrs Burroughs. The Flood. The rainbow … it was supposed to be a sign.
Burroughs. What of?
Mrs Burroughs. That God wouldn't destroy the world again.
Burroughs. He did though, didn't he?
Mrs Burroughs. Somebody did.

(She takes his arm)

Come on, Adam. Forget the past. We've a future to think of.